Hot Rod Hamster

To Abigail, Jessie, and Violet—C.L.

For Ron and Jane, who finally got
a hot rod of their own!—D.A.

Hot Rod Hamster

By
Cynthia Lord

Pictures by
Derek Anderson

MILO WAS HERE

TOMMY

WILLY

Good Boy!

WAG YOUR TAIL

Friday

ONE DOG'S JUNK

JUN

Scholastic Inc.
New York Toronto London Auckland
Sydney Mexico City New Delhi Hong Kong

Great day, grin day, build a car to win day,
Cheer day, chase day, gonna have a race day!

Old car, new car, shiny painted blue car,
Rust car, clean car, itty-bitty green car.

Which would *you* choose?

Smooth wheels, stud wheels, driving through the mud wheels,
Fat wheels, thin wheels, take her for a spin wheels.

Which would *you* choose?

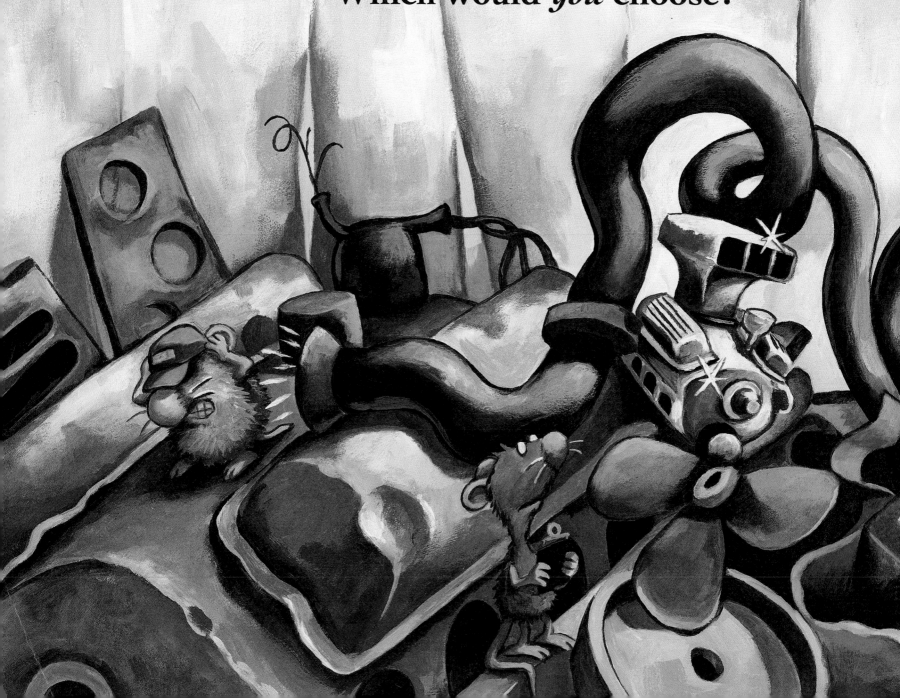

Coil parts, flat parts, gleaming this and that parts,
Round parts, straight parts, funny, out of date parts.

Which would *you* choose?

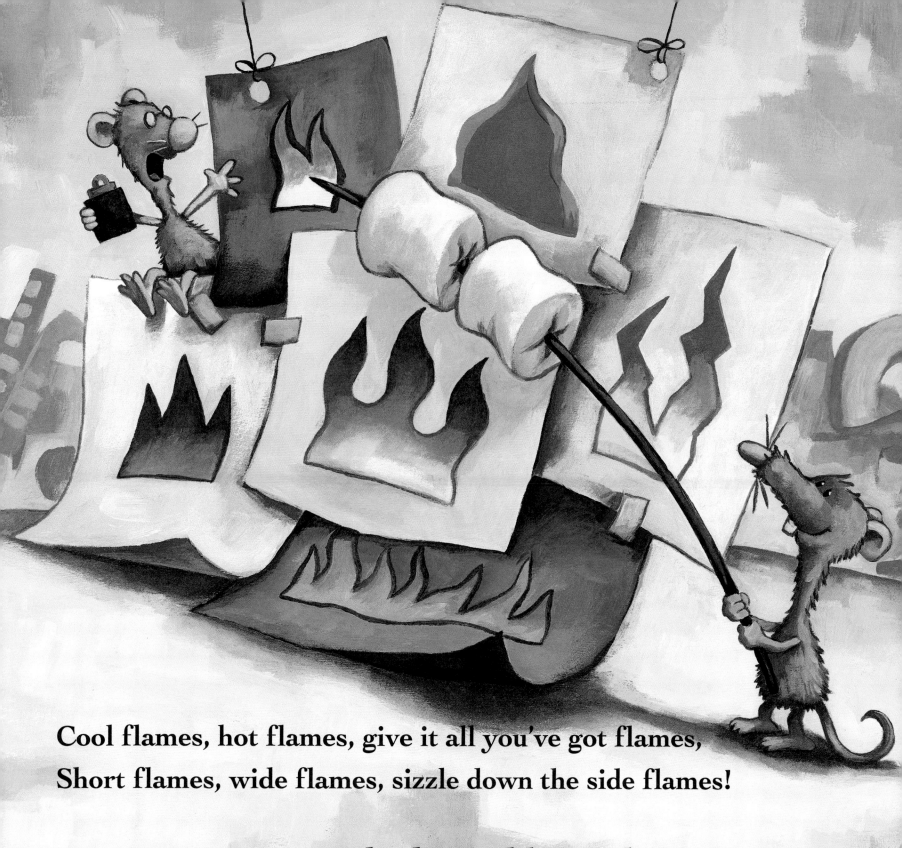

Cool flames, hot flames, give it all you've got flames,
Short flames, wide flames, sizzle down the side flames!

Which would *you* choose?

Stare face, scowl face, frowning grouchy-growl face,
Bored face, dare face, nose up in the air face.

Which would *you* choose?

Tough race, tight race, can't go left or right race,
"Oops!" race, "oh!" race, don't know where to go race!

Beep! Beep!

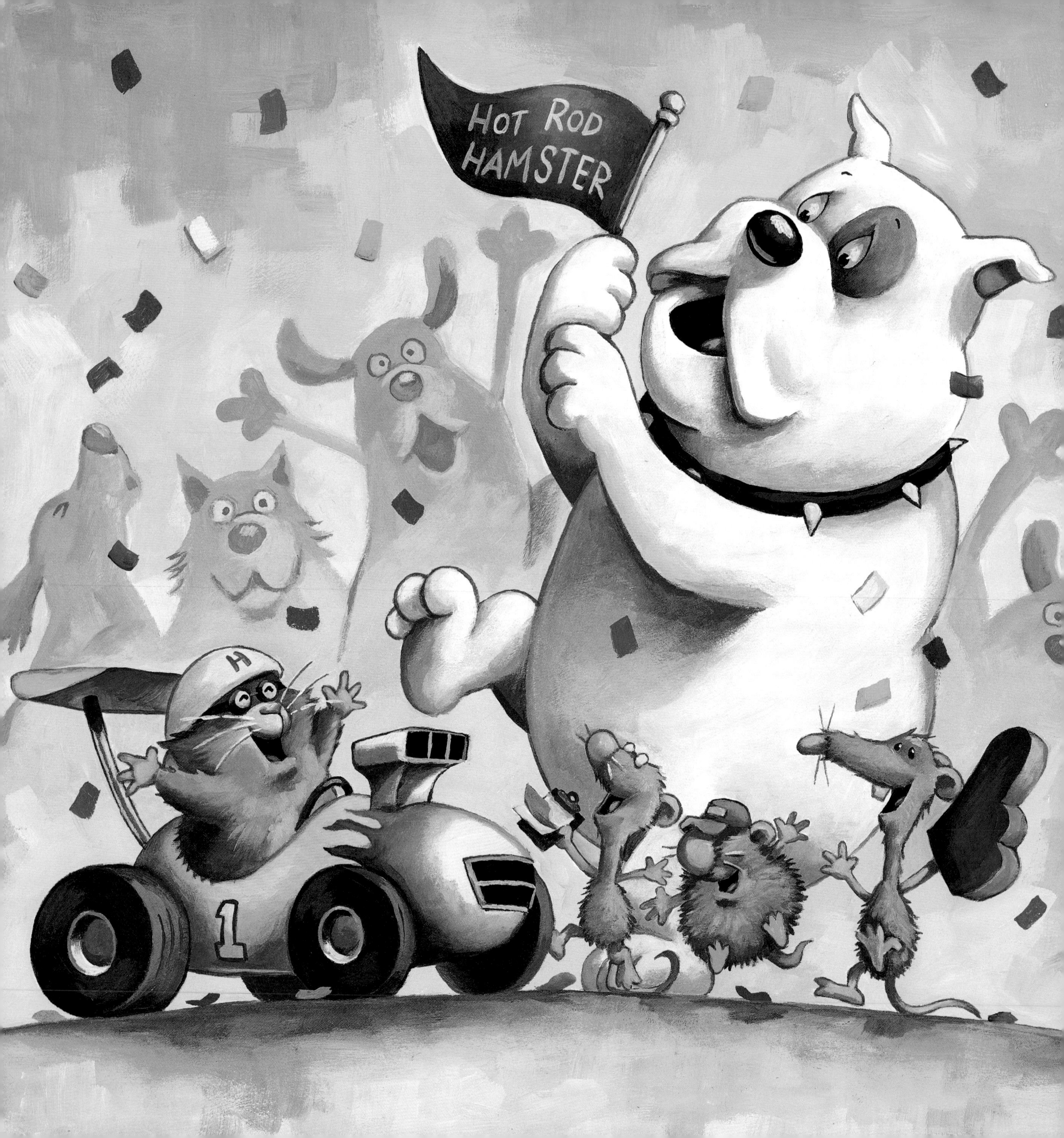
HOT ROD
HAMSTER
H
1

Crown prize, cup prize, cannot pick it up prize,
Silver prize, gold prize, lots of fun to hold prize.

Which would *you* choose?